6

RECREATION IN MATHEMATICS

RECREATION IN
MATHEMATICS

SOME NOVEL PROBLEMS

ROLAND SPRAGUE

★

Translated by T. H. O'Beirne

15039

NEW YORK
DOVER PUBLICATIONS, INC.

Blackie & Son Ltd., 5 Fitzhardinge Street, London, W.1
Bishopbriggs, Glasgow
Blackie & Son (India) Ltd., Bombay

Published in the United States of America by
Dover Publications, Inc.
180 Varick Street
New York, N. Y. 10014

Printed in Great Britain by Blackie & Son Ltd., Glasgow

FOREWORD

Mathematics can provide enjoyment for a variety of reasons—meeting the needs of those who seek recreation, while giving satisfaction to those who are intrigued by solving problems, close reasoning and unexpected solutions.

I offer here a selection of problems which for the most part are new. A few of them have had a limited circulation in specialist publications or in private communication. The problems all are appropriate additions to recreational mathematics and deserve to become more widely known in this connection. The majority of the solutions require only school mathematics for their comprehension.

The production of the English edition of my book *Unterhaltsame Mathematik* enables me to mention two points on which I am deeply indebted to H. E. Dudeney.

One is the last puzzle of this collection, intended to be a variation of Dudeney's problem about an English general who by an ingenious device succeeds in catching the fleeing army and its commander.

The other is as follows. It seems that in tutoring one of his pupils Dudeney must have dealt with the problem: to dissect a square into a finite number of squares, all different. He solved the problem, all but one piece which was oblong. In his tale, according to the gracious principle of compensation, it had to be of pure gold. It was this golden shortcoming that stimulated the first solution of the problem in 1939.

I have to thank Mr. T. H. O'Beirne for his clear translation. His amendments and clarifications have been made with the greatest care for the benefit of the non-mathematical reader. I must also thank Mr. C. T. Rivington who has looked after the publication details of this translation.

ROLAND PERCIVAL SPRAGUE

PUZZLES

SOLUTIONS

Puzzles

Siting a Central Depot

The street plan of a city consists only of straight streets intersecting at right angles, and at an odd number of the junctions there are kiosks. Figure 1 gives, as an example, a plan with ten streets and three kiosks. The occupants of the kiosks now wish to draw their wares from a common central depot. How should this be located so as to give a minimum total length for single trips to the depot from each individual kiosk? The breadths of the streets are to be neglected.

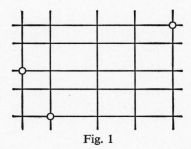

Fig. 1

2 Jumbled Wires

An electrical cable of n wires crosses a river. The ends of the wires are separated, on each bank, and there is nothing to indicate how they correspond. Show how to determine their correspondence with the help of a battery, a bell, and two sets of labels with numbers from 1 to *n*. Only one two-way crossing of the river is allowed, and the river itself is not to be used as a conductor.

<table>
<tr><td>3</td></tr>
</table>

Heavy Boxes

(1) Five equal cubical boxes, each with an *A* on its top side, stand together as shown in Fig. 2. The boxes are to be brought into line, but they are so heavy that they can be moved only by tipping them over about an edge. With these conditions, it proves to be impossible to bring them into line with the *A*'s all the same way up, and the arrangement finally achieved has a plan view as shown in Fig. 3. Which box originally was in the middle?

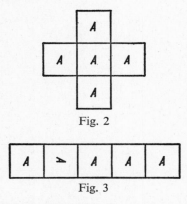

Fig. 2

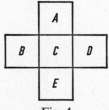

Fig. 3

(2) Boxes marked with different letters as in Fig. 4 have also to be brought into line; but here only four are as heavy as in the first problem —the fifth is empty, and easy to handle. The final arrangement is to

Fig. 4

4

have five boxes in line and to show a pattern *ABDCE* (with no rotations of the letters). Which is the empty box?

(3) If there are *two* empty boxes, we can change the arrangement of Fig. 4 into a linear alphabetical arrangement *ABCDE*. Which are then the two empty boxes?

4	*A Game with Four Numbers*

If we operate cyclically with any four whole numbers a, b, c, d, to form their difference set $|a-b|$, $|b-c|$, $|c-d|$, $|d-a|$, we obtain a new set of four (non-negative) whole numbers from which we can derive a third set, and so on.

For example the set of values $a = 5$, $b = 11$, $c = 0$, $d = 2$ leads to a table:

5	11	0	2
6	11	2	3
5	9	1	3
4	8	2	2
4	6	0	2
2	6	2	2
4	4	0	0
0	4	0	4
4	4	4	4
0	0	0	0

where the tenth row and every later row contain nothing but zeros.

Further trials with other numbers will suggest that a row of zeros arises sooner or later. If we replace the 11 by a 12, in our example, the four zeros arrive with the eighth row; but if we replace the 11 by any other whole number above 11, however large, the first row of zeros is always the seventh row.

(1) Must we in fact *always* reach a row of zeros? (2) If so, is there a number N such that in all cases the Nth row of the table—at the latest —has nothing but zeros?

(Warning! In the game with *three* numbers, the table beginning with 0, 0, 1, has *no* row of zeros.)

To write numbers, we nowadays use a procedure that involves ten different symbols—the digits from 0 to 9. We have learned, for instance, to denote the sum $3.10^3 + 0.10^2 + 9.10 + 7$ shortly and unambiguously by 3097, and a school child can verify that this number is the result of multiplying 163 by 19. The difficulty of the same operation with Roman numerals can be appreciated from the fact that in the year 1326 the production of a multiplication table from 1×1 to 50×50 by the then Rector of the University of Paris was counted as a significant scientific achievement.

There is no mathematical reason for the predominance of the number 10 in our number system. The novice calculator uses his ten fingers as an aid: and in English the symbols and the fingers are alike called 'digits'.

In a system which had 5 instead of 10 as the base, we would have $3097 = 4.5^4 + 4.5^3 + 3.5^2 + 4.5 + 2$, and must write it '44342', where now there are digits only from 0 to 4; here $5 = 1.5 + 0$ will be written as '10', and $55 = 2.5^2 + 1.5 + 0$ as '210'.

In a system with 2 as the base—the dyadic or binary system—there similarly will be only the digits 0 and 1, and one consequence is that the 'length' (or number of digits) for a number written in binary fashion —with a finite number of exceptions—will exceed the triple of its length in a decimal system.

Which of two numbers is the larger can be as simply appreciated in other systems as in the decimal system. If one number is longer than another, then it is the larger: in other cases we compare digits, reading from the left, and the larger number is then the number which first has a larger digit than the other, as comparisons are made for successive places. Thus 1100 is larger than 1011, whatever is the system in question.

How to add binary numbers is easily learned. One number is written under the other, just as in the decimal system; the work starts at the right-hand end, and attention is needed to the transfer of occasional 'carries' of 1 to the next following place to the left. The example

$$
\begin{array}{r}
11011 \\
+\ 1110 \\
\hline
101001
\end{array}
\qquad
\left(
\begin{array}{r}
27 \\
\text{Scale of ten:} +14 \\
\hline
41
\end{array}
\right)
$$

includes all points which require attention.

There is one question which can be answered for binary numbers although it still seems to be unanswered for decimal numbers. In the decimal system, if we add two numbers which show opposite sequences of digits, it can happen that the sum is a palindrome—that is, a number which has the same sequence of digits reading from the left as from the right. For example, the sum of 1030 and 0301 gives the palindrome 1331. It can however also happen that the sum is not a palindrome, as with $812 + 218 = 1030$; but here another reversal of digits and an addition leads to a palindrome—actually to 1331 as we just saw. The question at issue is whether *every* number sooner or later leads us to a palindrome in this way. For the binary system, the answer is 'no'; we can apply the procedure as often as we like to the binary number '10110' (the 22 of the decimal system) and we will never get a palindrome. How can this be proved?

6 | Shunting Operations

A railway line branches at a gentle slope into two sidings a, b (Fig. 5) which terminate in buffers. A train has an engine at its higher-level end, denoted by the arrow, and trucks—denoted by letters—are uncoupled singly or in groups, to roll into a or b according to the setting of the points. Then the engine shunts and assembles a new train, whose front and rear portions consist of the trucks from a and b respectively: this we call a 'manoeuvre'. The trucks have to be brought into alphabetical order by shuntings.

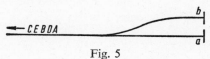

Fig. 5

For this purpose, we can take the 'word' provided and divide it into 'reading-sectors'; we consider the letters in alphabetical order, and begin a new reading-sector each time a leftwards shift of the eyes is required before a continuation. The reading-sectors of *CEBDA* are thus: $1, A$; $2, B$; $3, CD$; $4, E$. An evident shunting procedure involves letting the truck or trucks of the first reading-sector roll into a and all others into b. The trucks of the first reading-sector then come to their desired place behind the engine and need not be uncoupled in the following manoeuvres. In the second operation, all trucks of the second reading-sector go to *a*, all those in later reading-sectors to *b*. Then all the trucks of the second reading-sector get to their proper places. This continues up to and including the trucks of the second-last reading-sector: for if the trucks of this group are ordered correctly, the trucks of the last reading-sector will automatically form the end of the train.

The procedure described here thus needs a number of manoeuvres one less than the number of reading-sectors. In general, however, it will not solve problems where a minimum number of manoeuvres is made a requirement. Two such problems are:

(1) Show how the trucks in a sequence *CEBDA* can be ordered alphabetically in only two manoeuvres.

(2) The truck symbols form the word *INTERCHANGEABLE*; how many manoeuvres are required to arrange them alphabetically?

| 7 | *Red or Black* |

Six persons are subjected to a form of intelligence test, for which six calendar sheets are set out in a room. Each shows a different date in the same month. Week-days are in black and Sundays are in red (no holidays other than Sundays are considered). Before the first candidate (1) enters the room, one sheet is turned over. This candidate (1) is then asked if he can deduce the colour of the inverted sheet from a view of the other sheets. His answer—'Yes' or 'No'—is put on the back of the inverted sheet, with the number (1) attached. When (1) departs, (2) will enter; a second sheet will have been turned over, and (2) is asked whether he can deduce the colour of the second sheet from his predecessor's answer, together with the four visible sheets. This answer is noted in its turn. So it goes on. The sixth candidate sees only the backs of six sheets, five of which have inscriptions while one is still blank. He is asked whether the colour of the sixth sheet can be deduced from the previous answers.

(The test would be stopped if any candidate gave an erroneous answer.)

(i) Assuming that the sixth candidate finds nothing but 'No' answers, can he resist this mass of suggestion and give a 'Yes' answer?

(ii) After four 'No' answers there is a 'Yes'; and the last candidate is additionally informed that his sheet shows the 18th of the month. What should he say to this?

8 | The Problem of 12 Coins

Among twelve coins there is one at the most which has a false weight. With three weighings on an equal-arm balance, *but with no use of weights*, show how to establish whether there is a false coin, or not; and if so, which it is, and whether it is too light or too heavy.

9 | A Problem with 13 Coins

Of 13 coins one at the most has a false weight. By three weighings *with* use of *weights*, show how to ascertain:

(1) whether there is a false coin;
and if so,

(2) which it is,

(3) how much it weighs, and

(4) the true weight.

10 | Nim

Several heaps of counters are provided, and two players play alternately. Each move consists of selecting one of the heaps and either reducing it or removing it completely. The winner is the one who makes the final move. This well-known game is called Nim.

If there are only two heaps (or if only two heaps are left), the way to win is clear: the player who always makes the two heaps equal will thus ensure that he has the last move. With two heaps each containing n counters—we call this the position (n, n)—the first player consequently loses, if his opponent knows his business.

Positions where the player who makes the next move can be defeated will be known as losing positions, or shortly as L positions. The others—which are the majority—will be known as winning positions, or W positions. (This terminology is sometimes reversed, in the literature of recreational mathematics, on the grounds that the winner will be the one who sets up what we call an L position.)

Recognition of the L positions for Nim involves using a binary symbolism. If the numbers for positions are written in binary form, underneath each other as if for additions, then the L positions have an even number of units in each vertical column. For example (1, 2, 4) is a W position; for from

$$1 \sim 001$$
$$2 \sim 010$$
$$4 \sim 100$$

we in fact find an odd number of 1's in every column. The winning move is to remove the 1 in the left-hand column of the third row and simultaneously provide each of the other columns with a 1—that is, to reduce the heap of 4 to a heap of 3; and (1, 2, 3) is then an L position.

Another example of a W position is the position (5, 6, 7);

$$5 \sim 101$$
$$6 \sim 110$$
$$7 \sim 111$$

Here there are three winning moves. The 5 should be reduced to 1, the 6 to 2, or the 7 to 3; (1, 6, 7), (5, 2, 7) and (5, 6, 3) are L positions, by the previous criteria.

On the other hand, if some given position has an even number of 1's in every column—so that it is then an L position—any move will remove this property; for by each reduction of a binary number at least one 1 will be replaced by a 0, and in the column concerned there will then be an odd number of 1's. Every move will change an L position to a W position, and there is at least one move which can make a W position into an L position. The last L position, the position $(0,0,...0)$, brings victory to the player who produces it.

If we feel it is a blemish that Nim with only two heaps has so little mystery, we can improve things by making what might be called a 100 per cent dilution. We can play a game with counters on a staircase which has either three or four treads, where a move is agreed to be the removal of any number of counters from one step to the next lower, or else from the first step to the foot of the stair. It is then not so evident that the numbers on the first and third steps have to be kept equal by the player who is to have the last move and so win. If the staircase is higher, the number of counters on the steps with *odd* numbers will take over the role of the heaps in Nim. Here there will indeed be *increases* of heaps intermediately, but these increases become cancelled soon afterwards.

There is another game, played with counters on a row of cells, which is closely related to this staircase game. Each move here consists of advancing one of the counters to a position nearer to the beginning of the row, without occupying or passing over an already occupied cell. Once again two players play, and he who moves last is the winner.

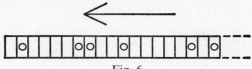

Fig. 6

(1) What is the winning move in the position illustrated in **Fig. 6**?

The game of Nim, with the trivial addition of allowing intermediate 'increasing' moves, has indeed a general significance for games between two players in which a limited number of alternate moves are ended by a move by the winner.

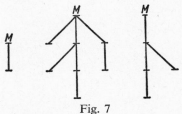

Fig. 7

Figure 7 shows an example. In this game, the displacement of one of the three markers *M* to a next lower point on one of the lines ranks as a move. The player who can no longer move loses.

(2) Who is the winner in this game?

| 11 | *A Property of the Number* $\sqrt{2}$ |

If we consider the numbers which are integral multiples of $\sqrt{2}$, namely $1 \times \sqrt{2}, 2 \times \sqrt{2}, 3 \times \sqrt{2}, \ldots$, paying no attention to the decimal parts of these numbers, we obtain a sequence of numbers

$$1, 2, 4, 5, 7, 8, 9, 11, 12, 14, \ldots$$

The numbers

$$3, 6, 10, 13, \ldots$$

are missing from this sequence. At the start of these sequences, we can see that the kth number of the second sequence is produced by increasing the kth number of the first sequence by $2k$; thus

$$3 = 1+1\times2, \ 6 = 2+2\times2, \ 10 = 4+3\times2, \ 13 = 5+4\times2$$

Is this relation valid generally?

12   *A Remarkable Tunnel*

Is it possible to cut a hole in a cube in such a way that a larger cube can be passed through the hole?

13   *A Draw for a Skat* Tournament*

In a skat club, the 24 members A, B, C, D, E, F, G, H, J, K, L, M, N, O, P, Q, R, S, T, U, V, W, X, Y, take part in a tournament. Three players are required at each table, and the tournament sheet provides the following groupings by numbers:

Round 1.   (1, 2, 3) (4, 5, 6) (7, 8, 9) and so on up to (22, 23, 24)

Round 2.   (1, 10, 22) (2, 14, 20) (3, 9, 18) (4, 16, 23) (5, 11, 17) (6, 12, 21) (7, 13, 19) (8, 15, 24)

As participants draw their numbers, the sets of players for each round—alphabetically listed—turn out to be:

For Round 1: *AJR, BKS, CLT, DMU, ENV, FOW, GPX, HQY*

For Round 2: *ANX, BHM, CDV, EGW, FKT, JQS, LPR, OUY*

Find the pairing of letters and numbers produced by the draw.

14   *Pieces to be Moved*

On a board consisting of a row of cells of any length, n pieces occupy separate cells. With each move, two players alternately transfer any

* *A German three-handed card game.*

single piece on to any free cell nearer the beginning of the row. (In contrast with a form of Nim mentioned in Problem 10, 'jumping over' is here permitted.) At the end, the pieces are to lie on the first n cells, and the player who brings about this arrangement is the winner.

The cells can appropriately be numbered $0, 1, 2, \ldots$. For $n = 1$ there is no problem. For $n = 2$, the losing positions (L positions) are given by $(e, e+1)$, where e is any even cell number: this is easy to show. For $n = 4$, each L position is also an L position at Nim: for in Nim each L position obtained from a W position which has four different numbers must likewise have four different numbers (for here two heaps should only be made equal if the other two heaps are already equal). Hence it follows for $n = 3$ that the L positions are identical with those of Nim, if we begin the numbering of the cells with 1 instead of with 0 (as if the row were prolonged to an earlier initial cell which was already occupied by a fourth piece).

Without proof we assert: for $n = 5$, the L positions are the same as L positions for Nim, if we restrict the series to 16 cells at the most, and number them with $0, 15, 14, \ldots 1$. Cell numbers then are *increased* during play—with one exception, the move to 0.

The play needs no mathematical knowledge if the cells are marked in appropriate fashion—for example by shading or colouring at the corners (Fig. 8). The directions for winning then become simply: play so that the cells occupied by the five pieces will together have 0 or 2 or 4 shadings at their left-hand lower corners, and similarly for each of the other corners. In Fig. 8, consequently, the middle one of the five pieces must move to the second cell from the left.

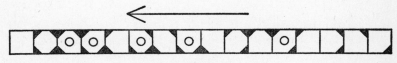

Fig. 8

In any game that must finish after a finite number of moves made alternately by two opponents, each position can be given a non-negative whole number as a *rank*. The rank is fixed so that from any position of non-zero rank, a position with *each* lower rank, but not one with the rank r itself, can be reached in *one* move, whether or not other positions of higher rank can be reached also: whereas for $r = 0$ only positions of higher rank are obtainable—or none if the position is a final one at

13

the end of a game. In this way, final positions are given the rank 0, and positions which lead only to final positions are given the rank 1; in general each position has as its rank the smallest number of the series 0, 1, 2, ... which is absent from the set of rank numbers for positions that can be obtained in a single move. In a game where the last player wins, the L positions are then defined by having the rank 0.

How the rank is to be calculated for the game of the travelling pieces was first discovered by C. P. Welter a few years ago. This requires a special, but quite simple, calculation procedure for which the sign $\oplus$ will here be chosen.

For two numbers in binary notation, a and b, pairs of digits in corresponding places are compared with each other and a 0 is written where they are the same, a 1 where they are different; this process gives a new number (in binary notation) which we denote by $a \oplus b$.

Evidently we have

$$a \oplus b = b \oplus a, \quad a \oplus a = 0, \quad 0 \oplus a = a$$

Example: $7 \oplus 9 = 14$, for

$$\frac{\begin{array}{l} 7 \sim 0111 \\ 9 \sim 1001 \end{array}}{14 \sim 1110}$$

The rank R of a position $(s_1, s_2, \ldots s_n)$—that is, a position which has pieces on cells with numbers $s_1, s_2, \ldots s_n$—is calculated step by step by two rules:

1. $R(s_1, s_2, \ldots s_n) = R(x \oplus s_1, x \oplus s_2, \ldots x \oplus s_n)$ for even n
$$= x \oplus R(x \oplus s_1, x \oplus s_2, \ldots x \oplus s_n) \text{ for odd } n$$

where x may be any positive integer (or zero). In practice we take $x = s_1$, so that we have $x \oplus s_1 = 0$ and can then apply Rule 2.

2. $R(0, s_2, s_3, \ldots s_n) = R(s_2 - 1, s_3 - 1, \ldots s_n - 1)$

We must forgo the proof of Rule 1 here. Rule 2 is almost self-evident: if one piece already occupies the cell 0, then in effect there are only $(n-1)$ pieces which travel on a series of cells that begin one cell further on. For $n = 1$ we have $R(x) = x$.

What rank has the position $(2, 3, 5, 7, 11)$?

15 | *A Dissection Problem*

Figure 9 shows two copies of the same right-angled triangle, whose area in one copy is divided by the altitude in the ratio $a:b$ ($a < b$), the whole being held to have unit area. The three portions thus have areas 1, a, b.

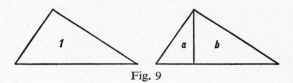

Fig. 9

Further copies of the triangle are to be divided into constituent right-angled triangles, by repeated insertions of altitudes in such a way that no two subdivisions have the same area, anywhere over the full set of copies. How many copies in all will this allow?

16 | *Two Round-table Arrangements*

Two table arrangements are to be found for n persons sitting round a circular table, in such a way that the separation of every possible pair will be altered when a change is made from one arrangement to the other.

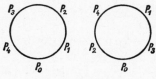

Fig. 10

For $n = 5$, with persons P_0, P_1, ... P_4, the problem can be solved as shown in Fig. 10. For $n < 5$, there are no such arrangements, nor are there any for $n = 6$.

For what values of n do such arrangements exist?

17   *Packets of Match-boxes*

Three match-boxes can be assembled to form a rectangular block in
three different ways, if all three are to be orientated identically. How
many shapes of rectangular packets are there for n match-boxes?

18   *A Set of Weights from Laputa*

In Gulliver's town of Laputa (which floated magnetically over the land),
the mathematicians recommended having new sets of weights in which
there were one each of 1, 2, 4, 8, . . . , and in general of 2^n grams ($n = 0$,
1, 2, . . . k). Each whole number of grams could be built up from these
—actually in a unique fashion (binary number system).

Their intention was perverted by an obvious type of mistake, arising
from inattention by the local sages, and sets of weights having one each
of n^2 grams ($n = 0, 1, 2, \ldots k$) were instituted instead; so in the boxes
there was a cylindrical depression provided for 0^2 grams, which
naturally remained empty. As not every whole number can be made
up by a sum of different squares (the numbers 2, 3, 6 cannot, for
instance) these sets of weights were useless, since a royal decree forbade
the practice of subtractive weighing. In an effort to save the situation,
the experts considered whether an auxiliary weight could be supplied
in the empty position in the box, to be used in the pan with the load
(by royal permission) in case of need. This demanded a weight of x
grams such that the numbers

$$2+x, \quad 3+x, \quad 6+x, \quad \text{etc.}$$

would be sums of different squares. The investigation showed the
existence of such numbers x, and the smallest of these was selected as
the number of grams for the auxiliary weight. Which was this?

19   *A Special Coinage System*

In a coinage system with pieces for 1, 2, 5, 10, 20, 50 units of money,
for instance, at least 6 coins are needed to make up 99 units. Find a
coinage system in which no amount from 1 to 100 units demands more
than two coins, with the number of different types as small as possible.

20 | Prices of Books

A hesitating book buyer is thinking of choosing six books out of eight, where the price of each book is a whole number of shillings, with none less than two shillings. The prices are also such that each selection of six books would cost the buyer a different sum. Finally his love of books overcomes his desire to economize and he buys all eight books. How much must he pay, at the least?

21 | Making Short Work of Division

Instead of dividing a certain whole number by 4, we can transfer the first digit from the left-hand end to the right-hand end of the number. What is the smallest number with this property? The same question is to be answered for divisors 5, 6, 19, 26, 91. Is there such a number for *every* divisor 2, 3, . . . ?

22 | A Still-unsolved Problem

To allow *n* objects of nearly equal weight to be ranked in order of weight, comparisons are made between various pairs, using a beam balance. How many such weighings are necessary? The problem becomes interesting for $n = 5$, and for higher values, but has not yet been solved completely.

23 | Lasker's Variant of Nim

It was Emanuel Lasker—for many years a world master of chess—who determined some of the strategic positions for the following variant of the game of Nim (see Problem 10): the player who has to move can either diminish one of the heaps, *or divide it in two heaps*, at his free choice. The winner is the one who makes the last move.

A position with two equal heaps is a losing position (*L* position) here just as in Nim. The player who sets this up has only to copy each subsequent move of his opponent to have the last move and so win. However, the position (1, 2, 3) in Nim is an L position, but is a winning position (W position) in Lasker's game: for the next to play divides the heap of 3, and copies each move of his opponent after thus producing the position (1, 2, 1, 2).

Examples of L positions are:

1, 2, 4	2, 3, 6	3, 4, 8	4, 5, 6	5, 7, 13
1, 3, 5	2, 5, 8	3, 7, 11	4, 7, 12	5, 9, 11
1, 6, 8	2, 7, 10	3, 9, 13	4, 9, 10	5, 10, 16

Lasker wrote: 'I have not found a rule which gives the disadvantageous positions. However, it seems to me that the rule is connected with the rule for Nim.'

His belief is in fact well founded, for the following theorem holds: a position in Lasker's game is an L position if and only if it becomes an L position for Nim when heap numbers $4k+3$ are increased by 1 and heap numbers $4k+4$ are reduced by 1, for all values $k = 0, 1, 2, \ldots$. How can this be proved?

24 'Odd' is the Winner

On a table there are 41 counters. Two players play alternately, and at each move each removes at the most seven counters (and at least one). The winner is the player who has an odd number of counters at the end.
Which player should win?

25 A Diophantine Problem

There are positive integers N which are such that the numbers N^3+1 have exact divisors of the type $aN-1$, where a also is a positive integer. For example, for $N = 1, 2, 3, 5$ we have

$$2 = 1^3+1 = (2 \times 1-1)(3 \times 1-1) = 1 \times 2$$
$$9 = 2^3+1 = (2 \times 2-1)(2 \times 2-1) = 3 \times 3$$
$$= (1 \times 2-1)(5 \times 2-1) = 1 \times 9$$
$$28 = 3^3+1 = (1 \times 3-1)(5 \times 3-1) = 2 \times 14$$
$$126 = 5^3+1 = (2 \times 5-1)(3 \times 5-1) = 9 \times 14$$

Are there any other numbers N of similar type?

26   *Notable Numbers in Human Affairs?*

Wilhelm Fliess has asserted in a book that all the numbers which are important in human life can be expressed mathematically in the form $23x + 28y$, where x and y are whole numbers. Since $23 \times 11 - 28 \times 9 = 1$, while every natural number is expressible as a sum of repeated units, the assertion is true—and likewise pointless. Even when we exclude negative values of x and y, only a finite set of numbers cannot be expressed in the form $23x + 28y$. Which is the greatest of these?

27   *A Property of the Harmonic Series*

The series $1 + \frac{1}{2} + \frac{1}{3} + \ldots + \dfrac{1}{n} + \ldots$ is called *harmonic*. Someone tries to find the value of its sum by adding terms in a calculation on paper; he is unsuccessful, since the sum can be made to exceed any given number, by taking a sufficient number of terms.

After becoming aware of this, he resolves to continue his work at least until for some n (other than $n = 1$) he comes upon an integral sum for $1 + \frac{1}{2} + \frac{1}{3} \ldots + \dfrac{1}{n}$. When will this be?

28   *A Meteorological Problem*

At each instant of time, are there two antipodal points on the earth's surface which have equal temperatures and also equal pressures?

29   *Historians on Television*

Each of the 17 members of a historical society writes to every other member. The exchanges between each pair are concerned with ancient, medieval or modern history—but with only one of the three. For a television programme, three historians are wanted whose mutual studies all involve only one of the three periods. The secretary of the society promises to look for such a trio in his card index; but he is unaware whether one exists, or how it could soonest be found. His first attempt in fact breaks down; the chosen Mr. *A* did indeed correspond with Messrs. *B* and *C* about ancient history, but the latter two were in correspondence with one another about modern affairs. How can the secretary be helped in his task?

30   *A Game for All Fools' Day*

In the diagram given in Fig. 11, two opponents each have one piece which they move from an intersection to an adjacent intersection. The diagram shows the starting position.

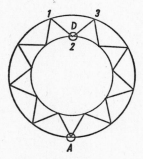

Fig. 11

The attacker *A* always has a free choice of four paths, but the defender *D* is limited to the points 1, 2, 3 of the 'fortress'. The first player is chosen by lot. The player *A* wins if he succeeds in occupying the point of the fortress on which *D* is situated: he loses if he moves into an unoccupied point of the fortress, or if he fails to penetrate it in reasonable time.

Who should win?

Solutions

1   *Siting a Central Depot*

This problem can legitimately be solved by counting votes—an unusual procedure in mathematics! The occupants of the kiosks can vote together whether the depot should be chosen to the north or to the south of any selected crossing A (Fig. 12). In the example given, they will cast one vote for north, and two for south. So B, the next southerly crossing from A, must next be considered and voted on; two occupants will vote against any further shift to the south. A westward shift

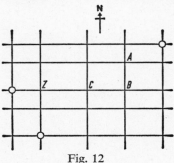

Fig. 12

however may still bring advantage. Votes for this will be $2:1$ in favour, and so the occupants next consider C. Moving westward, we see that the first crossing where the votes go against any further shift is Z, and this is the desired location for the depot. For three kiosks, the north-south street through Z is singled out as the one having at most one kiosk to either side of it; similarly for the east-west street through Z.

In the general case of $2k+1$ kiosks there will be at most k kiosks to either side of a street through Z, the location of the depot.

Why does the smallest sum of distances come from this point Z, which we can find almost instantaneously? Because for each shift away from Z by one block length a to the west or east, and then by one block length b to the south or north, the number of occupants whose journeys are increased by a is larger than the number of those whose journeys are reduced by a—and similarly for the shifts of length b. The sum of the journeys to the crossing Z thus increases at least by $a+b$. The location of Z is unaffected—surprisingly, perhaps—by some displacements of individual kiosks.

For an even number of kiosks the location of the depot is not in general uniquely defined. (Why not?)

It can readily be seen that taking account of street breadths raises no practical difficulty; by the same procedure we can determine the location of the depot uniquely as one of the four corners of the crossing Z already indicated.

| 2 | *Jumbled Wires* |

For $n = 1$ there is no problem, for $n = 2$ the problem is insoluble. Here is a procedure which works for all other numbers. A is the bank with which we begin: the other is B. First we assume n is odd.

At the end of the cable at A, leave one wire alone and connect the others in pairs. Go over to B, and determine which pairs are joined up at A and which is the unconnected wire. Call the unconnected wire No. 1, and join it to one member of any first pair; this latter is made No. 2. Make the other wire in this first pair No. 3 and connect it to the first wire in any second pair, which is made No. 4. Make the other wire in this second pair No. 5 and connect it to a No. 6 in any third pair. Continue until finally the second wire in the last pair remains unconnected; this receives the number n.

Go back to A and break the electrical joins, replacing them with non-conducting (or notional) joins, to indicate the associated pairs. There is now a connection at B joining the unpaired wire at A to exactly one other wire. So the unpaired wire is No. 1 and the other is No. 2. Then No. 3 is the associate of No. 2 at A, No. 4 is the associate of No. 3 at B, and so on.

Secondly, we suppose n is an even number greater than 2. Then leave one wire unconnected at *each* side and treat the remaining odd number of wires as just described; at B start with either of the two unconnected wires.

3   *Heavy Boxes*

If the boxes are thought of as dice with numbers on them (conventionally arranged so that pairs of numbers on opposite faces add up to 7) the sum of the numbers for the upper, front and right-hand faces of any of the dice is an odd or even number according to its orientation; for instance in Fig. 13 (assuming the face with the A has one pip on it) we have

$$1+2+3 = 6 \quad \text{(even)}$$
$$2+6+3 = 11 \quad \text{(odd)}$$
$$4+2+1 = 7 \quad \text{(odd)}$$

In this way we can call the orientation of a box either *odd* or *even*. The class of orientation changes each time a box is tipped over on an edge. Fig. 13 shows this for two cases—where the first box is tipped over backwards, or to the right. The result follows in the general case

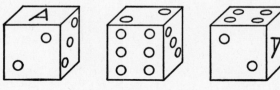

Fig. 13

from the fact that each tipping over of the box leaves two of the previous numbers to be considered again, while the third is replaced by its difference from 7 and thus becomes odd if it was even before, and conversely. So the sum of the upper, front and right-hand faces changes in similar fashion—the box goes from an odd orientation to an even one, or vice versa. It is not in fact difficult to show that successive tipping operations can indeed produce any even orientation on any square of unchanged colour and any odd orientation on any square of altered colour.

(1) If all the boxes in Fig. 2 are taken to have even orientations,

only the second from the left in Fig. 3 has an odd one; so the latter must have been tipped over an odd number of times, and the rest an even number of times.

Now we assume that all this takes place on a floor which is chequered like a chess-board, where each box exactly covers one square. Every time a box is tipped over, this changes the colour of the square which it covers; so each box stands on one colour in all its even orientations, and on the other colour in all its odd ones. Suppose that the first, third and fifth boxes are on black squares in Fig. 3; then they were on black squares in Fig. 2 also. The second box in Fig. 3, which is now on a white square, must in view of its new odd orientation have been on a black square, earlier, in Fig. 2. So we recognize these four boxes as those which occupied four like-coloured squares in Fig. 2—i.e. the outer ones. The second box from the right in Fig. 3, with an even orientation on a white square, stood also on a white square in Fig. 2, and so was in the middle.

(2) By arguments as in (1), one of A or B must be empty, since they first cover squares of the same colour, and then squares of different colours, with even orientations in both cases; similarly for one of B and C, one of B and D, and one of B and E. The empty box is therefore B.

(3) For the same reason as in (2), one at least of the following pairs must have been moved otherwise than by tipping it over: A or B; A or C; A or D; B or E; C or E; D or E. So the empties are A and E.

4	*A Game with Four Numbers*

The answer to (1) is 'Yes'; the answer to (2) is 'No'.

(1) If each even number in the four chosen numbers is denoted by e, and each odd number by o, the corresponding letters for every later row follow from these, since the difference of two odd numbers or of two even numbers is an even number, while differences in other cases are odd numbers. It is easy to show that four even numbers arise, at the latest, with the fourth formation of the differences.

Cases like $eeeo$ and $oooe$, where e's are replaced by o's and vice versa, can be taken together, since all their later rows correspond exactly. Also, only one of the cases $eeeo$, $eeoe$, $eoee$, $oeee$ needs to be dealt with, for these correspond by cyclic interchange of letters and of columns of the table. So it is sufficient to consider the cases *oooo*, *eeeo*, *eeoo*, and *eoeo*. For *oooo* the next row gives four even numbers, and this remains true throughout the rest of the table. From *eeeo* we have a succession of rows *eeoo*, *eoeo*, *oooo*, *eeee*. This indicates that after four formations of differences (at the most) all numbers will be even; the cases *eeoo* and *eoeo* are implicit in *eeeo*.

If however a row of the table has four even numbers—say $2a$, $2b$, $2c$, $2d$, the doubles of a, b, c, d—each later row of their scheme has double the number in the corresponding row of the scheme for a, b, c, d, since $\left| 2x - 2y \right| = 2 \left| x - y \right|$. Now the fourth row at the latest after a, b, c, d has only even numbers, so that the fourth row after $2a$, $2b$, $2c$, $2d$ has only numbers divisible by 4. This argument can be indefinitely repeated, to justify the assertion that in every such table the fifth row (at the latest) has four numbers divisible by 2, while the ninth has four divisible by 2^2 and the thirteenth has four divisible by 2^3; in general the $(4n+1)$th has four numbers divisible by 2^n. Since n can be chosen sufficiently large for 2^n to exceed all the numbers in the table, a contradiction is avoided only if we reach a row of zeros in every case.

(2) Consider a sequence of non-negative whole numbers, where from the fourth number onwards each number is equal to the sum of its three predecessors, and positive. Six successive numbers are then of the form

$$a_n, \ a_{n+1}, \ a_{n+2}, \ a_n + a_{n+1} + a_{n+2}, \ a_n + 2a_{n+1} + 2a_{n+2},$$
$$2a_n + 3a_{n+1} + 4a_{n+2}$$

The game with the *last* four of these numbers gives a table beginning

a_{n+2}	$a_n + a_{n+1} + a_{n+2}$	$a_n + 2a_{n+1} + 2a_{n+2}$	$2a_n + 3a_{n+1} + 4a_{n+2}$
$a_n + a_{n+1}$	$a_{n+1} + a_{n+2}$	$a_n + a_{n+1} + 2a_{n+2}$	$2a_n + 3a_{n+1} + 3a_{n+2}$
$a_{n+2} - a_n$	$a_{n+2} + a_n$	$a_n + 2a_{n+1} + a_{n+2}$	$a_n + 2a_{n+1} + 3a_{n+2}$
$2a_n$	$2a_{n+1}$	$2a_{n+2}$	$2(a_n + a_{n+1} + a_{n+2})$

and so three formations of differences lead to a row with the doubles of the *first* four numbers of the sequence. Doubling all the numbers in one row will double all later numbers, and the first arrival of a complete row of zeros will be unaffected. A table based on the *last* four of our six numbers will thus take three more rows to produce a row of zeros than will be required for a table based on the *first* four; so each time the chosen set of four numbers is displaced two steps to the right in the given sequence, this will require three more rows to reach a row of zeros.

If a start is made using the initial values 0, 0, 1, a sequence of this type will take the form

$$0, 0, 1, 1, 2, 4, 7, 13, 24, 44, 81, 149, \ldots$$

and since the passage from 0, 0, 1, 1 to 0, 0, 0, 0 requires three rows, six are needed from 1, 1, 2, 4, nine from 2, 4, 7, 13, and so on. There is thus no number N with the properties asked for. This can readily be generalized to cover rational fractions. If irrational numbers are permitted, we soon come to a row of zeros from 0, $\sqrt{2}$, π, e, for example; but we never reach this from 1, x, x^2, x^3, if x satisfies the equation $x^3 = x^2 + x + 1$ ($x = 1 \cdot 839 \ldots$): for numbers 1, x, x^2, x^3 then form part of a sequence formed by the rule given earlier, and the sequence can also be continued indefinitely to the left, with nothing but positive terms.

| 5 | *Number Systems and Palindromes* |

Applying the procedure four times to the binary number 10110 gives the number 10110100, with no palindrome arising intermediately. We shall write the latter number as $101_{(2)}010_{(2)}$, so that it becomes the case $n = 2$ of a general type of number $101_{(n)}010_{(n)}$.

We now show that four further steps applied to a number of this type will produce the numbers $101_{(n+1)}010_{(n+1)}$, with once again no palindrome arising intermediately. To make the addition more easy to perform, we write $101_{(n)}010_{(n)}$ in the equivalent form $101_{(n-2)}11010_{(n-2)}00$. The two first steps then give:

$$
\begin{array}{r}
101_{(n-2)}11010_{(n-2)}00 \\
+\ 000_{(n-2)}10111_{(n-2)}01 \\
\hline
110_{(n-2)}10001_{(n-2)}01 \\
+\ 101_{(n-2)}00010_{(n-2)}11 \\
\hline
1011_{(n-2)}10100_{(n-2)}00
\end{array}
$$

or, more conveniently for the next addition, $101_{(n-2)}110100_{(n-2)}00$. The third and fourth steps yield:

$$101_{(n-2)}110100_{(n-2)}00$$
$$+\ \ 000_{(n-2)}010111_{(n-2)}01$$
$$\overline{110_{(n-2)}001011_{(n-2)}01}$$
$$+\ \ 101_{(n-2)}101000_{(n-2)}11$$
$$\overline{1011_{(n-2)}110100_{(n-2)}00}$$

Thus, as asserted, we obtain $101_{(n+1)}010_{(n+1)}$ and no sum can be a palindrome, for all later numbers will have the forms 10...00 and 11...01, in strict alternation.

6 ## Shunting Operations

We can imagine that each truck is furnished with a table which indicates into which of the two sidings it is to go in each manoeuvre. To ascertain the final relative positions of two trucks T_1, T_2, we can compare their tables, as for example in the following three cases:

(1)	T_1	T_2		(2)	T_1	T_2		(3)	T_1	T_2
	a	a			b	a			b	a
	b	b			b	a			b	b
	b	b			a	b			a	a

In the first case T_1 and T_2 will remain in the same relative position as originally, since they both are handled alike. In the second case, T_2 will finally come somewhere behind T_1, since in the last manoeuvre T_2 goes to b, and T_1 goes to a; this is true independently of any previous manoeuvres. In the third case nothing can be affected by the two final shunts, where the tables correspond; but T_2 comes in front of T_1 at the first shunt, and nothing changes this afterwards. The decisive shunt is thus the last one in which the two tables differ. The truck which then goes to b will stay behind the other throughout all subsequent operations. If the tables are identical, the trucks keep their original relative positions.

A surprising relation with binary numbers arises if we replace a by 0 and b by 1, and then rotate the tables through 90°, making the right-hand digits correspond to the sidings for the first of the shunts.

(1)	110	T_1		(2)	011	T_1		(3)	011	T_1
	110	T_2			100	T_2			010	T_2

In (2), T_2 has the greater separation from the engine *because* its binary number is greater than the one for T_1, and in (3) it has the smaller one, *because* 010 is less than 011.

Accordingly, the following method gives the fewest operations. We give the trucks of the first reading-sector the number 0, those of the second the number 1, and so on, and we write each number in binary form vertically below the letter symbol for the corresponding truck, replacing digits 0 by *a* and digits 1 by *b*. (Successive binary digits from left to right should read *upwards* in the columns.) Then for Problem 6(1) we have the table:

2	3	1	2	0
C	E	B	D	A
a	b	b	a	a
b	b	a	b	a

and for Problem 6(2) the table:

4	5	7	2	6	1	3	0	5	2	1	0	0	4	1
I	N	T	E	R	C	H	A	N	G	E	A	B	L	E
a	b	b	a	a	b	b	a	b	a	b	a	a	a	b
a	a	b	b	b	a	b	a	a	b	a	a	a	a	a
b	b	b	a	b	a	a	a	b	a	a	a	a	b	a

Here we can just manage with three operations, since the number 7 requires three binary places. (If we gave all the *E* trucks the number 2, the truck labelled with the letter *T* would finally have a number 8; and since 8 needs four binary digits, we would need four operations.)

7 **Red or Black**

(i) If the first candidate writes 'No', he can have seen four red sheets at the most; for had there been five red sheets he would have had to write 'Yes', since a month has five Sundays at the most, and his own sheet would then necessarily have been black.

If the second candidate writes 'No', he can have seen at most three red sheets. With four red sheets he would have had to say 'Yes': for since the first candidate would also have seen them, the second sheet

—which he also saw—could not have been red, and the second candidate would then know it was black.

If the third candidate writes 'No', he can have seen at most two red sheets; for with three he would have had to say 'Yes', since the second candidate also saw these three; the third sheet would then have to be black. Correspondingly the fourth candidate can have seen at most one red sheet, and the fifth candidate none. So the last sheet must be black, and the sixth candidate arrives at the answer 'Yes'.

(ii) If the 18th of the month were a Sunday, the month could only have had four Sundays, and everyone else would have known this similarly to the sixth candidate. By analogy to the solution of (1), this would imply that the first candidate saw at most three red sheets, the second at most two, the third at most one, and the fourth none. But this would contradict the assertion that the 18th was a Sunday, for if so the last sheet—with this number—would then be red. So the last sheet has to be black and the sixth candidate can again say 'Yes'.

Note. If it is also stated that the 18th on the last sheet is a Wednesday, the sixth candidate can conclude from the answers of his predecessors that it must be the 18th of February in a common year (not a leap year).

8 *The Problem of 12 Coins*

It would be reasonable to suppose that the selection of coins to be placed in the scale pans in the second and third weighings must be dependent on the results of the earlier weighings. 'Branching' solutions can indeed be found in the literature of recreational mathematics. Nevertheless the supposition is erroneous; a choice of coins for all three weighings can be uniquely determined in advance, and surprisingly enough this can make the whole procedure become much more readily comprehensible.

We begin with the simplest problem of a similar type—namely, where we have three coins and two weighings (assuming otherwise identical conditions). For this case, we can immediately see a solution —namely one where we can consider the coins in any order, and in the first weighing put the first coin in the left-hand pan, with the second coin in the right-hand pan, whereas in the second weighing we have the first coin in the left, but the third coin in the right; that is, in symbols:

$$(1) \quad 1\,|\,2 \qquad\qquad (2) \quad 1\,|\,3$$

Our next problem is to distinguish the individual cases: if the *l*eft or *r*ight pan goes down, we shall briefly symbolize this with *l* or *r* in the respective cases, and we shall write a numeral 0 if there is a balance, indicating a weight difference of zero.

A weighings record *ll* then indicates that the left pan descended on both occasions. In this case coin No. 1 is too heavy, and we write 1^+.

On similar lines we complete the following table:

ll	1^+	0*r*	3^+	00	all coins good.
*l*0	2^-	*r*0	2^+		
0*l*	3^-	*rr*	1^-		

The cases *lr* and *rl* cannot arise unless more than one coin is false.

The symbols *l*, *r*, 0 and their combinations will also be used to provide position-indicators for the coins, and we shall assume they respectively indicate that the coin concerned lies in the left pan or in the right pan, or is not among those being weighed. In the weighings considered above, the coins 1, 2, 3 have sets of position-indicators, or 'programmes', according to a scheme: 1, *ll*; 2, *r*0; 3, 0*r*.

There is no danger of confusion between weighings records and position-indicators, as it will always be clear whether movements of scale pans or locations of coins are in question. Actually, there is an obvious connection: if a coin has, for example, the programme *l*0, and is too heavy, it will then produce the weighings record *l*0; if it is too light, however, it will produce the 'opposite' weighings record *r*0. In our three-coin problem, we have a converse result: if a weighings record takes a form *l*0, for instance, which does not form the programme for any of the coins, then the coin with the opposite programme —namely coin No. 2—must be too light.

The possible programmes for two weighings—associated in opposite pairs except in the last case, with coin numbers prefixed appropriately (for one programme)—are then as follows:

(1) *ll*	*l*0	*lr*	0*l*	00
rr	(2) *r*0	*rl*	(3) 0*r*	

The selection of programmes must evidently satisfy two conditions:

(1) At each weighing the number of coins in the left and right pans has to be equal.

(2) Only one programme can be selected from each pair: otherwise

it could not be decided whether one coin was too heavy or another coin too light.

The choice to which we were led in our last example fulfils both conditions.

By attaching one of the symbols *l*, *0*, *r*, at the right, to *ll*, to *r0*, or to *0r*, we obtain nine new programmes

1	*lll*	4	*r0l*	7	*0rl*
2	*ll0*	5	*r00*	8	*0r0*
3	*llr*	6	*r0r*	9	*0rr*

which satisfy both conditions for nine coins, in similar fashion. To these we can add three programmes 10 *lrl*, 11 *rl0*, 12 *00r*, derived from the not yet used pair *lr*, *rl*, and from 00. This leads to three weighings for 12 coins in the form:

(1)	1	2	3	10	4	5	6	11
(2)	1	2	3	11	7	8	9	10
(3)	1	4	7	10	3	6	9	12

Interpretation of a weighings record is then a simple matter. If the result is 000, all coins must then have the same weight. If the result is *r0l*, we look for a coin with programme *r0l*, find this to be coin No. 4, and conclude that coin No. 4 is too heavy. However, if the result is *0lr*, for example, we find no coin with this programme, and conclude that it is the coin with the opposite programme *0rl*—namely coin No. 7 —which then is too light. The extension to the analogous problem for 39 coins with four weighings, or for 120 coins with five weighings, and so on, is not difficult.

This solution can be applied when 13 coins are in question, if it is known that *exactly one* of them is false. The weighings result 000 then indicates that coin No. 13 is false—a unique case in which there is no indication whether the false coin is too heavy, or too light.

9	*A Problem with 13 Coins*

In a paper listed among the references on p. 61, C. A. B. Smith mentions this elegant problem without giving a solution; with the best of intentions he leaves this as a task for his readers. We can achieve success here if we list the possible programmes in alphabetical order (treating the numeral 0 as if it were a letter *o*), and then take the first 13 of these, in the form:

lll	7	*lol*	5	*lrl*	1	*oll*	6	*ool*	8
llo	10	*loo*	4	*lro*	12	*olo*	3		
llr	2	*lor*	13	*lrr*	11	*olr*	9		

Here we have put coin numbers beside the programmes, choosing an order for which the justification will appear later. By application of this table, the three weighings take the following form:

(1)	1, 2, 4, 5, 7, 10, 11, 12, 13	——————
(2)	2, 3, 6, 7, 9, 10	1, 11, 12
(3)	1, 5, 6, 7, 8	2, 9, 11, 13

Let *a*, *b*, and *c* be the weights in the right-hand pan which will establish a balance in each successive weighing; if weights are needed in the left-hand pan, these will count as negative weights. Also, we shall use *x* to denote the weight of a proper coin, and *y* to denote that of a false coin, if there is one. We now have to examine the individual cases.

If—and only if—there is no false coin, we have $a:b:c = 9:3:1$.

If coin No. 1 is false there are three equations

$$8x+y = a$$
$$4x-y = b$$
$$y = c$$

from which we have $a-2b-3c = 0$, and hence $x = \frac{1}{4}(b+c)$, $y = c$.

If coin No. 2 is false, we have

$$8x+y = a$$
$$2x+y = b$$
$$2x-y = c$$

whence we have $2a-5b-3c = 0$, $x = \frac{1}{4}(b+c)$, $y = \frac{1}{2}(b-c)$. And so on.

Later on, we tabulate these two cases, and the others also. In a practical application, we would have to check through a series of relations $a:b:c = 9:3:1$, $a-2b-3c = 0$, $2a-5b-3c = 0$, etc., to see which of them is satisfied, in order to derive from this the number of the false coin. Some saving of effort can take place here, in view of the relations we introduced earlier between the weighing programmes and the coin numbers; for these will ensure that the expression

$$A = \left| \frac{4a - 9(b+c)}{a - 3b} \right|$$

provides the number of the false coin, in a majority of the cases, and that it will take the indeterminate form $\frac{0}{0}$ when no false coin is present.

As exceptions we have

$A = \infty$ for coin No. 8 [here we have $4a - 9(b+c) \neq 0$, $a - 3b = 0$]
also

$A = 0$ for coin No. 9 [here we have $4a - 9(b+c) = 0$, $a - 3b \neq 0$]
and

$$A = \tfrac{5}{2} \text{ for coin No. 10}$$
$$A = \tfrac{11}{2} \text{ for coin No. 11}$$
$$A = \tfrac{13}{4} \text{ for coin No. 12}$$

These can be memorized, and the questions (1) and (2) can be answered without recourse to a table.

A	No. of false coin	x	y	A	No. of false coin	x	y
$\dfrac{0}{0}$	—	c	—	7	7	$\dfrac{b-c}{2}$	c
1	1	$\dfrac{b+c}{4}$	c	∞	8	$\dfrac{b}{3}$	c
2	2	$\dfrac{b+c}{4}$	$\dfrac{b-c}{2}$	0	9	$\dfrac{b+c}{4}$	$\dfrac{b-c}{2}$
3	3	c	$b-2c$	$\dfrac{5}{2}$	10	c	$b-2c$
4	4	c	$a-8c$	$\dfrac{11}{2}$	11	$\dfrac{b-c}{2}$	$b-2c$
5	5	$\dfrac{b}{3}$	c	$\dfrac{13}{4}$	12	c	$4c-b$
6	6	$\dfrac{b-c}{2}$	c	13	13	$\dfrac{b}{3}$	$\dfrac{2b-3c}{3}$

Example. Suppose that the results of the weighings are $a = 80$ grams, $b = 28$ grams, $c = 10$ grams.

We calculate

$$\left|\frac{4a-9(b+c)}{a-3b}\right| = \left|\frac{4\times80-9\times38}{80-3\times28}\right| = \left|\frac{-22}{-4}\right| = \frac{11}{2}$$

So coin No. 11 is false, and weighs $b-2c = 8$ grams, whereas each of the others weighs $\frac{1}{2}(b-c) = 9$ grams.

10 *Nim*

(1) The numbers of empty cells which separate pairs of adjacent pieces—taken in order from right to left towards the beginning— correspond to numbers of counters on the first, second, and higher steps of the staircase; for each move of a piece must increase an interval to the right by as much as it diminishes an interval to the left (beyond the last piece to the right there is an infinite interval which corresponds to the foot of the stair). So the number of counters on the first step is 1, on the second 5, on the third 2, on the fourth 0, on the fifth 4, and on the sixth 1. The steps with odd numbers then present the position (1, 2, 4). To achieve an L position, namely (1, 2, 3), the second piece from the left can be moved one cell backwards towards the beginning. Another possibility consists of moving the fifth piece five cells, similarly; this produces the L position (6, 2, 4) by an 'increasing' move.

(2) The points are labelled with numbers 0, 1, 2, ... in the follow-

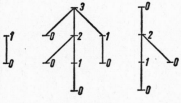

Fig. 14

ing fashion (Fig. 14). First, all end points receive a 0, and all points which *only* lead to end points receive a 1. Next, each point receives the smallest of the numbers 0, 1, 2, ... which cannot be found on an immediately adjacent point. After this the game may be seen to correspond to the position (1, 3, 0) for Nim. Each of the three separate 'trees' of the board corresponds to a heap, and labels have been introduced for the points on each tree in such a way that any move can either lead to any one of all the smaller labels, in the way that a heap can be diminished in ordinary Nim; or possibly to a label of higher value from which a label equal to the original label can be obtained by the next move—just as if we could increase Nim heaps in intermediate stages of the game.

So the first player wins provided he either moves the counter at numeral 3 to a new position on 1, or else makes an 'increasing' move by moving the counter at 0 to a new position on 2. In the first case he sets up the L position (1, 1, 0); and in the second case, the L position (1, 3, 2). (Cf. Problem 14.)

11 | *A Property of the Number $\sqrt{2}$*

Yes, the relation is general. We use the symbol $[x]$ to denote the greatest integer which does not exceed a given number x. Thus $[3{\cdot}5] = 3$, $[7] = 7$, $[-0{\cdot}4] = -1$. If g denotes a integer and x a positive non-integer, then

$$[g+x] = g+[x]$$

and, as is easy to show,

$$[g-x] = g-[x]-1$$

Provided that the assertion in question is true, the two sequences can thus also be written as

$$[k\sqrt{2}]$$

and

$$2k + [k\sqrt{2}] = [2k+k\sqrt{2}] = [k(2+\sqrt{2})]$$

where k has the values 1, 2, 3, . . .

We shall show that the sequences $[k\sqrt{2}]$ and $[k(2+\sqrt{2})]$, taken together, do in fact include every natural number exactly once. To do this, we choose any natural number n and calculate how many smaller numbers appear in each sequence: that is, we seek to find how many multiples of $\sqrt{2}$ and how many of $(2+\sqrt{2})$ are smaller than n. The first number is

$$\left[\frac{n}{\sqrt{2}}\right] = \left[\frac{n}{2}\sqrt{2}\right]$$

and the second is

$$\left[\frac{n}{2+\sqrt{2}}\right] = \left[\frac{n(2-\sqrt{2})}{2}\right] = \left[n - \frac{n}{2}\sqrt{2}\right] = n - \left[\frac{n}{2}\sqrt{2}\right] - 1$$

So the sum of these two numbers amounts to $n-1$.

If for example n is 10, then nine of the numbers less than 10 will appear in both series together (and they would be counted twice if they were to appear twice); if we now take $n = 11$ then ten of the numbers less than 11 will appear in both series together. The only possible addition to the previous numbers is then the number 10, and so 10 is included in exactly one of the two sequences. The same holds for every natural number.

12	*A Remarkable Tunnel*

If you give an answer 'No' without taking time to think, you probably have spheres in mind instead of cubes: for with spheres the negative answer would obviously be justified.

Fig. 15 shows a cube which we suppose to have unit length of edge. Four vertices are denoted by Q, R, S, T, and on certain edges there are points A, B, C, D such that $QA = QD = \frac{3}{4}$, and $TB = TC = \frac{3}{4}$. Then $AD = BC = \frac{3}{4}\sqrt{2}$.

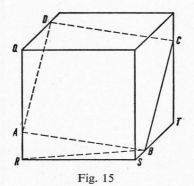

Fig. 15

The quadrilateral $ABCD$ is a rectangle, since the diagonals AC and BD are equal from the symmetry of the cube, and they bisect each

other at the centre of the cube. The theorem of Pythagoras shows that
$$AB^2 = AR^2 + BR^2 \quad \text{and} \quad BR^2 = RS^2 + BS^2$$
so
$$AB^2 = AR^2 + RS^2 + BS^2 = (\tfrac{1}{4})^2 + 1 + (\tfrac{1}{4})^2 = \tfrac{18}{16} = (\tfrac{3}{4}\sqrt{2})^2$$
and $AB = \tfrac{3}{4}\sqrt{2}$. Hence $ABCD$ is in fact a square.

If we let each of the points A, B, C, D move towards the centre of the cube by the same small distance, we then obtain a square which lies wholly within the interior of the cube: so a tunnel can be provided which has this square for a cross-section, without the cube falling apart. Now $\tfrac{3}{4}\sqrt{2}$ is equal to $1 \cdot 06066 \ldots$: thus it is possible to put a hole through a cube in such a way that another cube with a longer edge (about 6 per cent longer) can in fact pass through it.

---

13 | A Draw for a Skat Tournament

Instructions as in the tournament sheet can be given equivalently by a table of numbers whose rows indicate the groupings for the first round, and whose columns indicate those for the second round. A similar table with letters can show the groupings that result from the players' draw.

```
 1  .  .  2  .  .  .  3        A  J  R  .  .  .  .  .
 .  .  4  .  5  .  6  .        .  S  .  B  K  .  .  .
 .  7  .  .  8  .  9           .  .  L  .  T  C  .  .
10  .  .  . 11  . 12  .        .  .  .  M  .  D  U  .
 . 13  . 14  . 15  .  .        N  .  .  .  .  V  .  E
 .  . 16  . 17  .  . 18        .  .  .  .  F  .  O  W
 . 19  . 20  .  . 21  .        X  .  P  .  .  .  .  G
22  . 23  .  . 24  .  .        .  Q  .  H  .  .  Y  .
```

The above tables show the two sets of groupings involved in our problem. Both tables preserve their significance if rows are permuted in any fashion, or columns likewise. The question now is to determine permutations of rows and columns for, say, the right-hand table, in such a way that every letter moves to a position which in the left-hand table is occupied by a number.

If we consider a pair of rows (or columns) in either scheme, it may or may not happen that their six symbols occupy six different columns (or rows). A network diagram can be used to show for which row-pairs or column-pairs this holds, if we make points 1, 2, ... 8 correspond to the successive rows or columns, and then join these points in pairs by a line if and only if the associated rows or columns have the stated property. Both for rows and for columns, in the left-hand table we thus obtain the diagram given in Fig. 16.

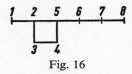

Fig. 16

For the right-hand table we have the diagram of Fig. 17 for rows and that of Fig. 18 for columns.

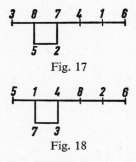

Fig. 17

Fig. 18

We now can, for example, determine the required number for A. Note that A stands in row 1 in the right-hand table and that point 1 in Fig. 17 corresponds to point 7 in Fig. 16: the number for A is thus in the 7th row of the left-hand table. A is also in the first column of the right-hand table, and point 1 in Fig. 18 corresponds to point 2 in Fig. 16: the number for A thus stands in the 2nd column in the left-hand scheme. In this way 19 is found as the number for A. We thus obtain the solution: A 19, B 11, C 3, D 18, E 8, F 22, G 15, H 5, J 21, K 10, L 2, M 17, N 7, O 23, P 14, Q 6, R 20, S 12, T 1, U 16, V 9, W 24, X 13, Y 4.

An identical row-and-column scheme of numbers can be employed in the following 'experiment'. The organizer gathers from the audience 24 different inscribed slips of paper, and makes a copy of their inscriptions for himself. Then he puts the slips in eight envelopes, three at a time, and they are delivered to a collaborator (the 'medium'), who opens any envelope and copies the inscriptions in a table, numbering those from the first envelope as Nos. 1, 2, 3, those from the second envelope as Nos. 4, 5, 6, and so on.

Then the slips are returned to the organizer, in eight envelopes, three at a time in an apparently random grouping, but one actually made in accordance with the tournament sheet for the second round. This then enables the organizer to reproduce his collaborator's numbered list with little delay.

 14   *Pieces to be Moved*

We have

$$R(2, 3, 5, 7, 11) = 2 \oplus R(2 \oplus 2, 2 \oplus 3, 2 \oplus 5, 2 \oplus 7, 2 \oplus 11)$$
$$\text{by Rule 1 with } x = 2$$
$$= 2 \oplus R(0, 1, 7, 5, 9)$$
$$= 2 \oplus R(0, 6, 4, 8) \qquad\qquad \text{by Rule 2}$$
$$= 2 \oplus R(5, 3, 7) \qquad\qquad \text{by Rule 2}$$
$$= 2 \oplus 5 \oplus R(5 \oplus 5, 5 \oplus 3, 5 \oplus 7)$$
$$\text{by Rule 1 with } x = 5$$
$$= 7 \oplus R(0, 6, 2)$$
$$= 7 \oplus R(5, 1) \qquad\qquad \text{by Rule 2}$$
$$= 7 \oplus R(5 \oplus 5, 5 \oplus 1) \qquad \text{by Rule 1 with } x = 5$$
$$= 7 \oplus R(0, 4)$$
$$= 7 \oplus R(3) = 7 \oplus 3 = 4 \qquad\qquad \text{by Rule 2}$$

By reason of its non-zero rank, the position (2, 3, 5, 7, 11) is thus a *W* position. In the search for the winning move, we first solve $R(2, 3, 5, 7, x) = 0$ to find $x = 15$, and then $R(2, 3, 5, x, 11) = 0$ to find $x = 19$. Both these solutions are useless, since play from 11 to 15 is impossible, likewise from 7 to 19. Ultimately from $R(2, 3, x, 7, 11) = 0$ we have the solution $x = 1$, and consequently the (unique) winning move is the moving back of a piece from cell 5 to cell 1. (This move we already found in a simple way for the restricted game of Fig. 8.)

A Dissection Problem

Only one more, as Fig. 19. A proof is as follows.

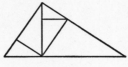

Fig. 19

Suppose a fourth copy of the large right-angled triangle, additional to the three in Figs. 9 and 19 could be subdivided into right-angled triangles all of which were different from each other and from those in the other three large triangles. The areas of all possible constituent right-angled triangles are the members of the sequence

$$1, \underline{a}, \underline{b}, \underline{a^2}, \underline{ab}, \underline{b^2}, a^3, \underline{a^2b}, \underline{ab^2}, b^3, a^4, a^3b, \ldots$$

and for a suitable choice of a these are all different from one another. We have underlined the members which are involved in Figs. 9 and 19.

The sum of the areas of the constituent triangles for four large triangles must amount to 4, *independently of a and b, so long as we have* $a+b = 1$. Similarly the sum of the triangles involved in Figs. 9 and 19 namely

$$1+a+b+a^2+ab+b^2+a^2b+ab^2$$

gives the value 3 on substitution of $b = 1-a$, and a no longer appears.

The sum of *all* terms of the sequence is the product of two infinite geometric series

$$(1+a+a^2+ \ldots)(1+b+b^2+ \ldots) = \frac{1}{1-a} \cdot \frac{1}{1-b}$$

If we put $a = \frac{1}{2}-d$ (with $d < \frac{1}{2}$), this sum takes the value

$$\frac{1}{\frac{1}{2}+d} \cdot \frac{1}{\frac{1}{2}-d} = \frac{4}{1-4d^2}$$

and this is more than 4, if $d > 0$. So we cannot include all the possible terms of the sequence when we have a set of only four large triangles. Also the sum of the terms included in a set of four large triangles would have to have a value of 4 quite independently of the value of a. So to find the total area we would be entitled to substitute $a = \frac{1}{2}$, even though the subdivision concerned would not then have all its triangles different. But the value 4 arises for $a = \frac{1}{2}$ only as a sum of *all* terms of the series. The assumption that a fourth large triangle can be divided in the way required thus leads to a contradiction.

16	*Two Round-table Arrangements*

Let the chairs remain fixed, numbered similarly to the persons who first take their places on them—in anti-clockwise order from 0 to $n-1$, say. Let the number of places through which the person P_k moves anti-clockwise for the second arrangement be called r_k—which we assume to be a number between 0 and $n-1$ inclusive. In the solution given for $n=5$, P_3 is moved 3 places anti-clockwise and thus sits in place 1 in the second table arrangement, since $3+3$ when divided by 5 gives a remainder of 1. In symbols: $6 \equiv 1 \pmod 5$. In words: 6 is congruent to (meaning, 'has the same remainder as') 1, modulo (meaning, 'for the divisor') 5.

The set of values of k is by definition the set of numbers from 0 to $n-1$ inclusive. The set of values of r_k must be the same set: for if two of the r_k were equal, for instance $r_x = r_y$, P_x and P_y would then keep their same distance apart. (An additional condition that *every* person should change his place could not in fact be fulfilled, since one of the symbols r_k must have the value zero.) Likewise the remainders of $k+r_k$ form the same set: these are in fact the place numbers for the second arrangement. Finally the set of remainders of $2k+r_k$ (for division by n) consists also of the numbers from 0 to $n-1$ inclusive: for if we had $2x+r_x \equiv 2y+r_y \pmod n$ it would follow that

$$x-y \equiv (y+r_y)-(x+r_x) \pmod n$$

and P_x and P_y would have the same separation in the two arrangements, only in opposite directions round the circle.

Since remainders modulo n for the four sets with members

$$k \qquad r_k \qquad k+r_k \qquad 2k+r_k$$

all consist of the numbers 0, 1, 2, ... $n-1$ in some order or other, their sums are identical, and likewise the sums of their squares: so we can write

(1) $\sum k \equiv \sum r_k \equiv \sum(k+r_k) \equiv \sum(2k+r_k) \pmod n$

(2) $\sum k^2 \equiv \sum r^2_k \equiv \sum(k+r_k)^2 \equiv \sum(2k+r_k)^2 \pmod n$

where summation is from $k = 0$ to $k = n-1$.

Disregarding the outer relations in (1), we have

$$\sum r_k \equiv \sum (k+r_k) \quad (\text{mod } n)$$

whence it follows that

$$\sum k \equiv 0 \quad (\text{mod } n)$$

and so $\sum k$ must be a multiple of n. But the sum of the numbers from 0 to $n-1$ amounts to $\frac{1}{2}n(n-1)$, and so is a multiple of n if and only if $\frac{1}{2}(n-1)$ is a whole number, in which case n must be odd.

Expanding the terms in the later relations of (2) leads to

$$\sum r_k^2 \equiv \sum (k^2+2kr_k+r_k^2) \equiv \sum (4k^2+4kr_k+r_k^2) \quad (\text{mod } n)$$

whence, by subtracting twice the middle expression from the sum of the other two, we obtain

$$2\sum k^2 \equiv 0 \quad (\text{mod } n)$$

and so $2\sum k^2$ must also be a multiple of n. But the sum of the squares of numbers from 0 to $n-1$ amounts to $\frac{1}{6}n(n-1)(2n-1)$; so we have $2\sum k^2 = \frac{1}{3}n(n-1)(2n-1)$, and if this must be a multiple of n, it follows that $\frac{1}{3}(n-1)(2n-1)$ must therefore be a whole number, which is true if and only if n is not divisible by 3.

By combining these two results we deduce that the required table arrangements are impossible if n is divisible either by 2 or by 3.

If on the contrary the number n is such that it is divisible neither by 2 nor by 3, we need only put $r_k = k$ to attain our objective. Each person is then made to go as many steps to the right as there are units in his number.

The values of k are the numbers $0, 1, 2, \ldots, n-1$; the values of $k+r_k = 2k$ are $2 \times 0,\ 2 \times 1,\ 2 \times 2, \ldots 2 \times (n-1)$; and the values of $2k+r_k = 3k$ are $3 \times 0,\ 3 \times 1, 3 \times 2, \ldots 3 \times (n-1)$. If $2x$ and $2y$ were to give identical remainders on division by n, then n would have to divide $2x-2y$ or $2(x-y)$, and likewise $x-y$ also, since n is odd. This is not possible if x and y are two different numbers from the set $0, 1, 2 \ldots n-1$. Similarly we conclude that the set of remainders of 3×0, $3 \times 1, \ldots 3 \times (n-1)$ is also identical with the set of numbers $0, 1, 2, \ldots n-1$, if n is not divisible by 3.

The round-table problem for $n(>1)$ persons is thus solvable when, and only when, the number n is divisible neither by 2 nor by 3.

If l denotes the number of boxes which are aligned by their longest dimensions to form, for example, the lower front edge of the block, with b the number of boxes grouped breadthwise to form the lower left-hand edge, and h correspondingly the number of layers, then $lbh = n$. In the case of $n = 3$, our table gives the three possibilities we mentioned

l	b	h
3	1	1
1	3	1
1	1	3

If n is a prime number p, then the table has only the three rows $p, 1, 1$; $1, p, 1$; $1, 1, p$.

In general, the question arises: in how many ways can n be split into three factors, when regard is to be paid to the order of the factors?

First let $n = p^a$. In this case the question can also be expressed: in how many ways can a articles (the a factors p) be divided into three groups (for l, b, h)? It is assumed that the articles are indistinguishable, but that the groups are to be treated as different, and are also to be allowed to be empty (in which case a factor 1 will appear as one of the three factors).

If we introduce a notional separator between the first and second groups, and likewise one between the second and third groups, as additional articles, we then have the simple question: in how many ways can we select a pair from $(a+2)$ articles (the pair being in fact a means of specifying positions for the two necessary separators)? The answer is, in $(a+2)(a+1)/2$ ways: this can be seen immediately if we consider the $(a+2)$ articles to be arranged in a definite sequence.

If n, divided into prime factors, has the form

$$n = p^a q^b r^c \ldots$$

the division of the b articles denoted by q is then independent of that of the a articles denoted by p; similarly for the other prime powers. So the number sought is then the product

$$\frac{(a+2)(a+1)}{2} \cdot \frac{(b+2)(b+1)}{2} \cdot \frac{(c+2)(c+1)}{2} \ldots$$

Every number in excess of 128 is expressible as a sum of unequal squares. This can be shown by writing * the numbers from 129 to 249 as sums of this type, when only 1, 4, 9, 16, 25, 36, 49, 64, 81, 100 need be used as the squares to be summed. For example

$$129 = 100+25+4, \ldots 249 = 100+81+64+4$$

This involves a sequence of 121 successive numbers. If we increase each of these by the number $11^2 = 121$, we then have the numbers from 129 to 370 expressed as sums of different squares, with 121 as the largest square which is involved. This sequence has 242 numbers, which is more than $12^2 = 144$. By addition of 144 to the last 144 members of this sequence we obtain a new and longer sequence. This procedure can be repeated indefinitely since from $n = 3$ onwards, $2n^2$ is greater than $(n+1)^2$.

Only the numbers in a certain finite set are impossible to obtain with the Laputan set of weights, namely the numbers

2, 3, 6, 7, 8, 11, 12, 15, 18, 19, 22, 23, 24, 27, 28, 31, 32,
33, 43, 44, 47, 48, 60, 67, 72, 76, 92, 96, 108, 112, 128

It will be found that differences between pairs of these numbers can express all the numbers from 1 to 46, but that no such difference can produce 47. This means that if the number a cannot be expressed as a sum of different squares, it follows that the number $a+47$ can be: and that 47 is the smallest number with this property. The number selected was thus 47.

---

* *It suffices to express the numbers 129 to 192 in this way, since the relation $1 + 4 + 9 + \ldots + 100 = 385$ implies that any expression for* n *leads to another for 385 − n.*

For example, from

$$136 = 100 + 36$$

we find immediately that

$$249 = 81 + 64 + 49 + 25 + 16 + 9 + 4 + 1.$$

19   *A Special Coinage System*

An obvious suggestion is to have regard to the decimal system, and choose values

    1, 2, 3, 4, 5, 6, 7, 8, 9, 10, 20, 30, 40, 50, 60, 70, 80, 90

with 18 types of coins involved.

We can improve on this result if we take 50 units as the highest piece, and arrange that when we have a value a we also have a value $50 - a$. If a value x less than 50 is representable as $b + c$, it follows that a value $100 - x = (50 - b) + (50 - c)$ must likewise be representable. With this procedure 17 values will serve, namely

    1, 2, 3, 4, 9, 14, 19, 24, 26, 31, 36, 41, 46, 47, 48, 49, 50

and indeed only 16 will suffice with the less regular system

    1, 3, 4, 9, 11, 16, 20, 25, 30, 34, 39, 41, 46, 47, 49, 50.

20   *Prices of Books*

To each choice of six things out of eight there corresponds an omitted pair, and conversely. Thus the prices for pairs are all different, too.

The three lowest possible prices are 2, 3, 4 shillings, and the next number must be 6 at least, since $5 + 2 = 3 + 4$.

If each time we look for the smallest possible next higher price, we obtain the sequence 2, 3, 4, 6, 9, 14, 22, 31, with the sum 91.

But this procedure does not necessarily also produce the lowest sum: as contrary evidence* we have the sequence 2, 3, 4, 6, 10, 15, 20, 30, with sum 90.

21   *Making Short Work of Division*

We first assume that the required number begins with the digit 1, and after this we need nothing other than simple division operations:

            1 divided by 4 gives remainder 1, quotient **0**;
            hence we continue with 10

---

* *Communicated by Gerhard Simon (1958). Dr. Fritz Düball has since found a sequence 2, 3, 4, 6, 10, 16, 21, 26 with sum 88.*

> 10 divided by 4 gives remainder 2, quotient **2**;
> hence we continue with 22
>
> 22 divided by 4 gives remainder 2, quotient **5**;
> hence we continue with 25
>
> 25 divided by 4 gives remainder 1, quotient **6**;
> hence we continue with 16
>
> 16 divided by 4 gives remainder 0, quotient **4**;
> hence we continue with 4
>
> 4 divided by 4 gives remainder 0, quotient **1**;

Result: $102564 \div 4 = 025641$. This is the smallest number of this type, since with other initial digits we likewise require six steps to come back to the initial digit as a quotient with remainder 0.

In general, for division by d, remainders ranging from 0 to $d-1$ are possible, and quotients ranging from 0 to 9: that is, $10d$ cases in all. Two of these cases single themselves out from the rest. One is 'remainder 0, quotient 0', and the other is 'remainder $d-1$, quotient 9': for these will repeat continually when calculations are continued forwards to the right and also backwards to the left. Each intermediate result determines both a succeeding and a preceding digit: consequently no so-called 'pre-recurrent' portion (as in recurring decimals) is here possible. The number sought thus has $(10d-2)$ digits at the most. The maximum is in fact attained for $d = 2$ and likewise for $d = 3$; also for $d = 6$, where the solution begins with 10169491 and has 58 digits. The other numbers asked for are:

> for $d = 5$: not 102040816 ... with 42 digits, but 714285
>
> for $d = 19$: not 100529, but 703
>
> for $d = 26$: not 100386, but 702
>
> for $d = 91$: 1001

There are numbers like this for every value of d.

22	A Still-unsolved Problem

A ranking in order of weight requires (as a maximum)

1 weighing for 2 objects,

3 weighings for 3 objects,

and   5 weighings for 4 objects,

since we can first put three of the objects in order, and then compare the fourth with the middle one of the three, and next with either the lightest or the heaviest, as found to be appropriate.

To insert a fifth in an established series of four, if we are unlucky, can require another 3 weighings, so that for 5 objects in the general case it might seem that 8 weighings would be required. However, we can proceed otherwise and succeed in every case with 7 weighings.

The objects and their weights can be denoted by a, b, c, d, e, in such a way that the first two weighings (in one order or the other) give $a < b$ and $c < d$, with the third giving $b < d$, so that we have $a < b < d$.

The fourth and fifth weighings can bring e into the order as a fourth with a, b and d, while the sixth and seventh can do the same with c: for c has to be ordered with respect to three things at the most, namely a, b and e, since $c < d$ is already known.

If W_n denotes the necessary number of weighings for n things, there then are 2^{W_n} possible comparison results, and $n!$ possible orderings. Hence we must have $2^{W_n} \geqq n!$; and for $n = 5$ we see that we have $2^7 = 128 \geqq 120 = 5!$.

However, it is not yet known whether W_n is always equal to the smallest number with this property. It has actually been conjectured that 12 things need no less than 30 weighings, although the fact that $2^{29} > 12!$ suggests that 29 might suffice.

---

23 *Lasker's Variant of Nim*

Proof of Lasker's conjecture requires the use of methods which we have used earlier for Problems 10 and 14. These methods apply to all games which have two characteristics:

(1) Two players must play alternately, and obviously one player or the other must have the first move: but elsewhere the rules must apply in absolutely identical form regardless of which player is concerned. The game must be equivalent to a board game which is played with *markers*, all of which are equally at the disposal of either player in turn (as distinct from what happens in the more usual type of board game, where each player has *pieces* of his own, which he can move but which his opponent cannot). At every stage of the game, the allowable moves must be defined in terms of some property which can be completely determined from the state of the markers *alone*, independently

of which of the players has to make the next move: this must be true also of the manner of deciding when the game is over, and which player is then the winner.

An onlooker newly arriving at a game of this type could therefore begin to consider what the next player could—or should—do next, without having to ask (or know) which of the players would be making the next move—an inquiry which would be necessary if the game were chess, for instance. Another consequence is that the joint effect of two successive moves may in some cases change the state of the markers in a manner which could equally well have arisen in one move, with a different choice for the earlier of the two moves; and in this event the only difference between the two cases—subsequently—is an exact exchange of the roles and prospects of the two players.

(2) It must be possible to think of the game as being composed of a number of *component* games which are played simultaneously. Each move in the actual game must then be the equivalent of selecting one of the component games—with complete freedom of choice—before making a move in this component game alone: and when a player is unable to move in *any* of the component games, this must imply that the game is then over, with the player concerned identified as the *loser*.

(Usually—and in our examples here—the rules will be identical for all the component games. This makes for simplicity, and a compact form of general rule may then be somewhat easier to find: but similar methods can be used even if the component games vary in type. In all cases, however, it must be the *winner* who makes the final move which leaves no move available for his opponent.)

In Nim, each component game can be taken to be the reduction of a single heap. In other games which we have discussed, we can have component games for each step of the stair, for each counter on the board, or for each of the three 'trees' of Fig. 7. In these cases the number of components remains constant, whereas in Lasker's game we shall see that it may increase; but this raises no difficulty.

The method we use depends on finding a way of assigning a 'rank' to each position in a component game. (See also Problem 14, p. 13.) The ranks are required to have the properties of the labels we introduced for the game of Fig. 7 (where the labels are in fact the ranks for the component games on the individual trees). Final positions must have rank 0, and every other position is to have a rank such that positions *of every lower rank* can be obtained at the next move.

The reason for this is that we can then find a way to determine a rank for the actual game by combining ranks obtained individually for each of the component games. When the overall rank is 0, the position is an L position, otherwise not; and this then shows how the actual game should be played.

When the component games for ordinary Nim are each the reduction of a single heap, it is easy to see that the rank of any position in any component game is exactly equal to the content of the heap; for the allowable moves then can lead to every position of lower rank. Arguments similar to those we used in discussing L positions and W positions for Nim in Problem 10 will then show that the overall rank is appropriately obtained by combining individual ranks according to the law of combination for which we used the symbol $\oplus$ in Problem 14. It will be seen that we shall have an overall rank of 0 in every case where our earlier rule identified an L position.

Ordinary Nim is the simplest game of this type precisely *because* the heap numbers and component ranks are then identical; but any *other* game of our chosen type can be regarded as equivalent to playing ordinary Nim with heaps whose contents are the component ranks. Since every lower rank can be reached in the real game, every lower heap number can be reached in the Nim representation. There is one minor point of difference from conventional Nim—a move may in fact *increase* a component rank. But this means only that at some intermediate stage, a Nim player can *increase* a heap—and the rules will permit his opponent to restore it as it was, with the next following move; and ultimately all heaps will still have to be removed completely.

When the rules allow a heap to be divided—as in Lasker's Nim—we must work backwards from small heaps to large heaps, in determining ranks for individual heaps. The combination rule as defined for the $\oplus$ sign can then be applied to give appropriate ranks for all the successor positions for any single heap; and after this the rank for the single heap can be appropriate determined.

We can now apply these methods to Lasker's Nim. We shall use numerals in parentheses to specify heap numbers in the actual—Lasker—game, and numerals without parentheses for the corresponding ranks, which we shall at times consider to be heap numbers for an ordinary game of Nim.

A heap (1) has as unique successor the ultimate heap (0) with rank 0. Thus (1) receives the rank 1.

A heap (2) has three successors: firstly (1); secondly (0); and thirdly, by division (1, 1). The ranks of (1) and (0) are respectively the corresponding numbers 1 and 0; and (1, 1) has the rank 0, since its only successor has the rank 1. The possible successors of (2) thus have the ranks 1 and 0: so (2) receives the rank 2.

A heap (3) has the four successors (2), (1), (0) and—by division—(1, 2). The ranks for these are 2, 1, 0 and 3: for there are components of ranks 1 and 2 in the position (1, 2), and the rank of (1, 2) in Nim has the value 3. So among the successors of (3), jointly, the ranks 2, 1, 0 and 3 appear: so (3) receives the rank 4.

A heap (4) leads by reduction to (3), (2), (1) and (0), whose ranks are 4, 2, 1, 0, respectively: and by division to (1, 3) and (2, 2), which have components with ranks 1, 4 and 2, 2. The position (1, 4) has in Nim the rank 5, and (2, 2) has the rank 0. Since positions with ranks 0, 1, 2, 4, 5 can be reached from (4) in one move, (4) receives the rank 3.

Continuing with this analysis leads to a conjecture of the following relationship:

Heap	Rank	
$(4n+1)$	$4n+1$	
$(4n+2)$	$4n+2$	$(n \geqq 0)$
$(4n+3)$	$4n+4$	
$(4n+4)$	$4n+3$	

To establish this—and so solve our problem—we have two things to prove:

(1) that this relationship will ensure that every move changes the rank of a position; and

(2) that this relationship will ensure that each position of any rank can have a position of every lower rank as an immediate successor.

Proof of (1). It is evident that each reduction of a heap will change its rank. So the question remains only for the case of divisions of heaps. The above relationship would provide all even heap numbers, and only these, with ranks which on division by 4 would leave the remainders 2 or 3: in binary notation, therefore, these ranks would have a 1 in the second place from the right.

If an *even* heap is divided, the result is two even or two odd heaps. Their ranks would provide for Nim a position where the heap numbers in binary form provided either two 1's or no 1's in the second column from the right. The rank of this Nim position would have a 0 in the second place from the right, where the rank of the parent heap had a 1.

The rank of an *odd* heap, in binary form, would have a 0 in the second place from the right, for the remainder on division by 4 must here be 0 or 1. By division, one odd heap and one even heap would appear, whose ranks would produce for Nim a position where the heap numbers in binary form displayed one 1 and one 0 in the second column. The rank of this Nim position would have a 1 in the second place from the right, where the rank of the parent heap had a 0.

Proof of (2). In general a lower rank can be arrived at by diminishing a heap. This becomes impossible only if we want to go from rank $4n+4$ to rank $4n+3$. In this case the heap $(4n+3)$ should be divided into $(1, 4n+2)$ or into $(2, 4n+1)$, which have identical ranks. Either pair has in Nim the wanted rank $4n+3$.

24 *'Odd' is the Winner*

The second player is the winner. The losing positions for the first player are the numbers $16m+9$, of which 41 is an example. A proof can be derived from the following table, whose scheme of rows repeats itself after 16 rows.

A		Z	A		Z	A		Z
0	*e*	*e*	8	*o*7	*o*	16	*e*7	*e*
1	*o*1	*e*	9	*e*1	*o*	17	*o*1	*e*
2	*o*1, *e*2	–	10	*o*2, *e*1	–	18	*o*1 *e*2	–
3	*o*3, *e*2	–	11	*o*2, *e*3	–			
4	*o*3, *e*4	–	12	*o*4, *e*3	–			
5	*o*5, *e*4	–	13	*o*4, *e*5	–			
6	*o*5, *e*6	–	14	*o*6, *e*5	–			
7	*o*7, *e*6	–	15	*o*6, *e*7	–			

The row labelled with 0 asserts that with a total of 0 counters the first player A and second player Z alike have an even number of counters, namely zero.

The row labelled with 1 indicates what is equally obvious—that with only one counter available, A acquires an odd number for the taking away of 1 counter (hence 'o1'), and Z will have an even number. In the next row (for 2 counters) A has a choice for the first time. If he takes 1, he puts himself in the place of the Z of the previous row (for 1 counter)—before A of the previous row makes his move—where under Z there is an e. He thus secures $1+e$ counters, that is o counters: hence o1. If he takes 2, he is then in the situation of Z of the top row, where likewise there is an e, and he receives in all $2+e$ counters, an *even* number: hence here we have e2. If A at will can make his total collection even or odd in number, Z has no possibility of having his choice of e or o: this is what the dash indicates in the column under Z.

Up to 7 counters the process is truly simple. With 8 counters, A dare not take less than 7, otherwise he would put himself in the position of Z in a row with a dash; by taking 7 however he becomes like the Z of the row labelled 1, and secures an odd number with $7+e$. This is the meaning of o7.

The entries o in the Z column for 8 and 9 counters arise from the fact that for both rows all seven preceding rows in the A column provide an o, and thus Z can be sure of obtaining an odd number when he plays.

The length of the period, namely 16, is not yet established in the table: for this purpose we have to continue the table by a few more rows, and then note that the set of the seven first rows repeats itself after the eighth row, with interchange of o and e. Seven successive rows in fact determine unambiguously the subsequent course of the table. Owing to the period of 16, the play for 41 counters is similar to that for 9 counters. If A with his first move takes

$$1 \text{ or } 2; \ 3 \text{ or } 4; \ 5 \text{ or } 6; \ 7$$

then Z will correspondingly take

$$7; \ 5; \ 3; \ 1.$$

Then either 32 or 33 counters are left, and these numbers have properties corresponding to the 16 and 17 of rows which are present in the table; so Z now makes for an e, since he already has an odd number of counters in his collection. If the winner is to be the one with the even number of counters, it can be seen that the scales are again weighted against Z, in a different but no more lenient fashion. Here, too, the starting numbers which favour him are a small minority.

More generally, if h is the largest allowable removal, the period is given by $h+2$ for even h, and by $2h+2$ for odd h.

25 *A Diophantine Problem*

We have first to note that if N^3+1 has a factor $aN-1$, where $N>1$, the remaining factor *must* then be of a similar type, such that we may write it as $bN-1$. (We are assuming that N, a and b are all positive integers.) For if we assume that the other factor is $bN-x$, with $0 \leqq x < N$, we have

$$N^3+1 = (aN-1)(bN-x)$$
$$= abN^2 - bN - aNx + x$$

and hence

$$x-1 = N(N^2 - abN + ax + b)$$

which is possible only when we have $x = 1$, and also

$$N^2 - abN + (a+b) = 0$$

The last relation is a quadratic equation which implies that N must be derivable from a and b in the form

$$N = \tfrac{1}{2}\{ab \pm \sqrt{[a^2b^2 - 4(a+b)]}\}$$

which requires that the integer

$$\Delta = a^2b^2 - 4(a+b)$$

must be a perfect square; and since a and b are both positive, Δ must be a square which is smaller than a^2b^2.

The next lower squares to a^2b^2 are

$$q_1{}^2 = (ab-1)^2 = a^2b^2 - 2ab + 1$$

and

$$q_2{}^2 = (ab-2)^2 = a^2b^2 - 4ab + 4$$

but we cannot have $\Delta = q_1{}^2$, since

$$\Delta - q_1{}^2 = 2ab - 4(a+b) - 1$$

is necessarily an *odd* number, and so cannot take a value of zero.

It follows that we must have $\Delta \leqq q_2{}^2$, and from

$$a^2b^2 - 4(a+b) \leqq a^2b^2 - 4ab + 4$$

we obtain

$$ab - (a+b) - 1 \leqq 0$$

equivalent to
$$(a-1)(b-1) \leqq 2$$

This last result shows that a and b cannot *both* exceed 2: it is then sufficient to consider the two cases $a = 1$ and $a = 2$, since a and b are involved symmetrically in the problem.

Using $a = 1$ we find that
$$\Delta = b^2 - 4b - 4 = (b-2)^2 - 8$$

has then to be a square. The only pair of squares which differ by 8 are 9 and 1; from these we have $(b-2)^2 = 9$, $\Delta = 1$, and then from $a = 1$, $b = 5$ we establish that either $N = 3$ or $N = 2$.

From $a = 2$ we find that
$$\Delta = 4b^2 - 4b - 8 = (2b-1)^2 - 9$$

then has to be a square. There are only two pairs of squares with difference 9—namely 9 and 0, likewise 25 and 16. The first choice leads to $(2b-1)^2 = 9$, $\Delta = 0$, and hence to $a = 2$, $b = 2$, $N = 2$; the second choice leads to $(2b-1)^2 = 25$, $\Delta = 16$, and so to $a = 2$, $b = 3$, with either $N = 5$ or $N = 1$.

This covers all possibilities, and shows that *no* other cases can be added to those which were given as examples in the statement of the problem.

| 26 | *Notable Numbers in Human Affairs?* |

If we say that a number m is *expressible* in terms of a and b when $m = ax + by$ can be solved with non-negative values of x and y, then the following result holds for a and b relatively prime: if
$$m + n = ab - a - b$$

exactly *one* of the numbers m and n is expressible.

In the identity
$$ax' + by' \equiv a(x' - bt) + b(y' + at)$$

t can be chosen so that $0 \leqq x' - bt \leqq b - 1$ holds.
So for
$$m = ax + by, \quad n = au + bv$$

we can suppose that

$$0 \leqq x \leqq b-1, \; 0 \leqq u \leqq b-1$$

From $m+n = ab-a-b$ we have

$$ax+by+au+bv = ab-a-b$$

whence it follows that

$$ab-a(x+u+1)-b(y+v+1) = 0 \qquad (1)$$

and so $x+u+1$ must be divisible by b.

The assumptions about x and u give

$$1 \leqq x+u+1 \leqq 2b-1$$

Thus since $x+u+1$ is a multiple of b we must have

$$x+u+1 = b$$

and then from (1) above we have

$$y+v+1 = 0$$

Consequently just one of the numbers y and v is negative, and the other is either positive or zero. The smallest expressible number is evidently 0 (for the case $x = y = 0$), since it is obvious that no negative number can be expressible. But the argument applies even if one of m and n is negative: so the largest number which is not expressible must have the value $ab-a-b$. For $a = 23, b = 28$ this is the number 593.

| 27 | *A Property of the Harmonic Series* |

We accompany Mr. Someone a small part of his way and hope for a useful idea.

$$1+\tfrac{1}{2} = \frac{2+\mathbf{1}}{2}, \quad 1+\tfrac{1}{2}+\tfrac{1}{3} = \frac{6+\mathbf{3}+2}{6}$$

$$1+\tfrac{1}{2}+\tfrac{1}{3}+\tfrac{1}{4} = \frac{12+6+4+\mathbf{3}}{12}$$

$$1+\tfrac{1}{2}+\tfrac{1}{3}+\tfrac{1}{4}+\tfrac{1}{5} = \frac{60+30+20+\mathbf{15}+12}{60}$$

$$1+\tfrac{1}{2}+\tfrac{1}{3}+\tfrac{1}{4}+\tfrac{1}{5}+\tfrac{1}{6} = \frac{60+30+20+\mathbf{15}+12+10}{60}$$

It turns out that in each numerator there is one single odd number which stands among others that without exception are even. If this always applies for the sum of any number of terms we will finish always with an odd sum in the numerator and, since the common denominator has at least one factor 2, we can then assert that the sum of n terms in the series will always have a fractional part, resulting from the division of an odd number by an even number.

How many times, in fact, does the common denominator contain the factor 2? Exactly k times, where 2^k is the highest power of 2 which appears in the sequence 1, 2, 3, . . . n. All other numbers up to n will include a factor 2 either less often or not at all. So a process of changing to the least common denominator will give even-valued numerators for the fractions with all denominators other than 2^k, but the fraction $1/2^k$ will have an odd-valued numerator. Mr. Someone can therefore never reach his objective.

| 28 | *A Meteorological Problem* |

Strange to say, yes. The following argument may serve to make this answer at least plausible. We start by considering any pair of antipodal points on the earth which at the instant of consideration have different temperatures: we use A to denote the point with the higher temperature, and A' to denote the one with the lower temperature. We now imagine another sphere—with reference lines for latitude and longitude—on which the warmer of two antipodal points on the earth is made to appear as land, and the colder as sea. The point A then appears on the new sphere in a land region A_1, which may be a continent, or only a small island, and A' is on the surface of a mass of water A_1' antipodal to A_1, where this may perhaps be only a pond. In every case A_1 will possess a coastline and A_1' a verge.

If this coastline and verge are identical, they form a curve which includes an antipodal point for each of its points, and this curve is in a single piece, similarly to an elastic band. Failing this, there must be a water region and a land region A_2 and A_2' which respectively surround A_1 and A_1', and these give rise to another verge and another coastline. If these should coincide, we here have a loop-curve with the antipodal property. Otherwise we must go on with A_3 and A_3', and so on. Here each A with an odd suffix denotes a land region, and each

A with an even suffix a water region (with any *A'* it is the other way round).

This procedure will in practice come to a stop, since we cannot go on dividing a globe indefinitely. Even if we assume that the globe is continually expanded, the accuracy of temperature measurement imposes another restriction. We must content ourselves with this intuitive basis for asserting that there is on the earth's surface a curve which consists of only one piece, which contains the antipodal point of each of its points, and which in fact includes nothing but point pairs which have identical temperatures (for the instant of consideration).

On the curve we choose any two antipodal points *B*, *B'* which have different barometric pressures (Fig. 20). We now introduce analogous

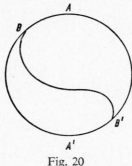

Fig. 20

considerations to obtain a corresponding loop-curve related to the pressure. It then becomes clear that these two curves will cut one another actually in a pair of antipodal points. (They cannot avoid intersecting once at least; and the antipodal point to any intersection must also be on both the curves.)

29	*Historians on Television*

Choose any member *A*. Since *A* writes to sixteen associates, he must therefore write to at least six of them about some one of the three periods —let us say the ancient period. If among these six there are two whose mutual exchanges are also devoted to ancient history, an acceptable trio has been found.

If not, these six members must mutually concern themselves with only two of the three periods. Let one of these members be *B*. Mr. *B* then writes to the five others about only two periods, and about one of these—let us say the medieval period—he must write to at least three of them. If two of these three write to each other about medieval matters, we then have an acceptable trio. If not, these three must mutually concern themselves in pairs with modern affairs, and thus here too we find a trio of the wanted type.

30 A Game for All Fools' Day

He who starts will lose. This can be seen if we use a symbolism for the points of the board as shown in Fig. 21.

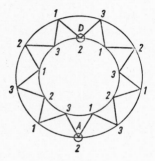

Fig. 21.

At the beginning, the points on which the pieces lie have equal numerals. The first move will make these unequal. The second player wins if he always restores equality of the numerals.

If we refer to the paths which lie between the circles as *transverse* paths, the equalizing of the numerals derives from a rule: 'Play in such a way that the number of transverse paths which lead back to the opponent is a multiple of 3.'

A trick here is later to substitute a board of similar type where the number of points is not divisible by 3. In this case the defender can apply the rule only for one of the two routes of transverse paths which connect him to the attacker, and the latter wins when he goes round the other way—no matter whether he is the first player or the second player.

Bibliography

The numbers preceding the items refer to the problems and their solutions:

2   Problem No. 29, *Archimedes*, **2** (April 1949), p. 10.

4   Freedman, Benedict, 'The four number game,' *Scripta Math.*, New York, **14** (1948), pp. 35–47.

6   Sainte-Laguë, A., 'Avec des nombres et des lignes (Récréations mathématiques),' Paris (1937), pp. 16–19, 27.

8, 9   Smith, C. A. B., 'The counterfeit coin problem,' *Math. Gaz.*, **31** (1947), pp. 31–39.

10   Bouton, C. L., 'Nim, a game with a complete mathematical theory,' *Annals of Mathematics*, Harvard, U.S.A., (2), **3** (1901–2), pp. 35–39.

11   Wythoff, W. A., 'A modification of the game of Nim (1906),' *Nieuw Archief voor Wiskunde* (2), **7** (1907), pp. 199–202.

14   Welter, C. P., 'The theory of a class of games on a sequence of squares, in the terms of the advancing operation in a special group,' *Nederl. Akad. Wet. Proc.* (A), **57** (1954), pp. 194–200.

16   Pólya, G., 'Über die "doppelt-periodischen" Lösungen des *n*-Damen-Problems,' in W. Ahrens, 'Mathematische Unterhaltungen und Spiele', **2**, Leipzig (1918) pp. 364–74.

17   Problem No. 1193 (by Sós, Budapest), *Zeitschrift für math. u. naturwiss Unterricht*, **65** (1934), p. 49.

22   Ford, Lester R., Jr., and Johnson, Selmer M., 'A Tournament Problem,' *Amer. Math. Monthly*, **66** (1959), pp. 387–9.

23   Lasker, Emanuel, 'Brettspiele der Völker,' Berlin (1931), pp. 183–6.

26   Fueter, R., 'Synthetische Zahlentheorie,' Berlin and Leipzig (1925), p. 7.

27   Problem by J. Schur in F. Neiss, 'Einführung in die Zahlentheorie,' Leipzig (1925), p. 104.

28   Steinhaus, H., 'Mathematical Snapshots,' New York (1960), p. 303.

3

Date Due

JAN 7 1980			
FEB 2 3 1981			